MAX YOUR MEMORY FOR EXAM SUCCESS

A WORKBOOK OF TOP TIPS AND ADVICE

Published in the United Kingdom by:

Exam Max Ltd,
Rotherby House,
Main Street,
Singleborough,
MK17 0RF

Exam Max is a limited registered company Reg. No:09594887
www. exammax.co.uk

First published 2015
ISBN 978-0-9933449-0-9

British Library Cataloguing-in-Publication Data: a catalogue record for this book is available from the British Library.

Cover and internal design: Martin Lore Partnership
www.martinlore.co.uk

Diagrams: Stephen Fletcher

Every effort has been made to fulfil requirements with regard to reproducing copyright material. The author and publisher will be glad to rectify any omissions at the earliest opportunity.

Printed and bound in Great Britain by IngramSpark Ltd, Milton Keynes, UK

MAX YOUR MEMORY FOR EXAM SUCCESS
A WORKBOOK OF TOP TIPS AND ADVICE

Dr Stephen Fletcher

Exam Max Ltd, Singleborough, Bucks, UK

Contents

Acknowledgements

Publishing a book is never a quick or a solo affair. It is a team effort. I am indebted to all the people who have helped to ensure the success of this project – a big 'Thank you' to everyone.

In particular my thanks go to:

- Les Bird and Terry Colbourn for believing in my vision of a 'Learning-to-learn' workshop and for then letting me run it with their trainee drivers. The experimental data from these sessions formed the cornerstone of this book
- Tricia Williams for her wisdom, invaluable guidance, and for her prayers
- Carly Newman for preparing some early drafts of the book. You deserve an extra thank you for persisting in the translation of the tricky Mind Maps!
- Sadie Garner and the students from Itchen College, Southampton for letting us test some key workbook concepts

The production team
- Martin Lore for his superb, creative design skills that have made this book visually appealing and an easy read
- Cameron Law for our 'Nutty Professor'
- The editing guys – Helen Jones and Andy Evans. For the many corrections!

Finally a massive thank you to my wife, Sophie, who has tirelessly project-managed this workbook through to publication. Thank you, Sophie for making my 20-year dream of publishing a book come true.

Introduction

A lack of advice on how to use your memory

When I went to school in the UK in the 1960s and 1970s there was little advice from my teachers on what I could do to improve my memory for exams. In fairness to them they might not have known either. So I spent hours just reading and re-reading my study material, hoping it would stick. In 2013 when I ran workshops in organisations for trainees on how to improve their memories during training, I was told little had changed. Some of those trainees had received some good advice, but they were certainly the exception.

There is now a wealth of ideas and psychological research available that can help us improve our memories. We no longer have to learn information by repeatedly going over and over it, hoping it will somehow stick in our memory. This in itself can be very boring and repetitive. In fact, learning and revising can be fun.

This workbook has been designed to share those ideas and research. It provides you with top tips and guidance on what you can do to help improve your memory for exams, and practical exercises so you can see your progress.

Will this workbook really work?

For a few years now I have been running a one-day 'learning to learn' workshop for trainees in the UK rail industry. These trainees embark on intensive training that lasts over 30 weeks. The train company invests over £100k per trainee. So it is important they succeed. Many of the tools and techniques in this book are based on those workshops. The feedback I get from the vast majority of my trainees on the day is extremely positive and when I meet many of them later in their training, they tell me how the tools and techniques have really helped. That makes me feel that I've made a difference and helped those trainees to not only succeed, but to succeed well.

Exams – you can't get away from them

Exams are an important part of modern life. As a young person in the UK you might be sitting your GCSEs, AS or A level exams. You may need top grades to get into university. At university you will need to sit and pass your exams to get a good degree. Post-degree you might also have to sit professional qualifications to achieve professional status. Some jobs such as being a fighter pilot, an air traffic controller, a financial adviser, a telecommunications engineer or a train driver will involve you sitting and passing training courses to demonstrate your competence. Even later in life a career change may mean re-training and further exams.

Why are they so important?

Many of us would say we don't necessarily enjoy being tested or examined. In fact, the experience can often be stressful. I remember after my degree having a recurring nightmare where I turned up for an important exam without having revised and was unable to answer any of the questions!

Taking and passing exams demonstrates what someone has learnt and understood during their training. Exam success shows the person is worthy of the certificate or accreditation and is competent or knows their stuff. This is important when it comes to work. I want to know that the mechanic who has fixed my car has done so safely so that my brakes don't fail. I want to be assured that my financial adviser is giving me the best financial advice as to where I should put my savings, and when I go under the surgeon's knife, I want to be confident that I am safe in her hands.

So exams are important and we can't get away from them. We have to show through our exam answers what we know and understand. The key to doing our very best in exams is a good memory. This is where this workbook can help. I say 'can' help because there is no guarantee that what I explore with you will definitely work, but there's a good chance that it might.

How this workbook works

Memory exercises
People love to check if a theory works so I've included some short memory exercises for you to try out along the way. These will show you how your memory works and give you some insight into what you can do to improve it. As you put some of the techniques into practice, you will see your scores improve!

Building blocks
I've called the first set of techniques 'building blocks'. These are the core foundation stones that I believe will help to improve your memory. There are five in total but you may find some work better for you than others. That's OK. Just use those that work for you.

Key and lock
I've called the second set of techniques 'key and lock'. There are five different memory keys which will help to unlock your memories. As with the memory building blocks, some may work for you and others may not, but give each one a go and see how you get on.

Top tips boxes
There are lots of practical suggestions throughout the workbook which are summarised in boxes called 'top tips'.

'Extra' psychology fact boxes
These contain some evidence or background to the theories or just a reference to lead you to extra information, should you want to find out more.

That's all the preamble – now let's get started!

BUILDING BLOCK 1

WORK HARD TO IMPROVE YOUR MEMORY

In weight training there is a common saying: 'No pain, no gain'. This is similar to developing a good memory. There is no instant success. However, if you practise the techniques in this workbook, then there is a good chance that your memory will improve. This is likely to pay dividends in the long run and you could get a massive return on your investment in time. This could include exam success or improvement in your exam grades. However, you need to find the memory techniques that work for you. That will take time and effort. It's a bit like achieving success at the Olympics. If you want to have a gold medal memory, then you will need to train hard.

Don't slip back into old ways of learning

I had a guy on one of my workshops who was in his mid-forties. He had changed career completely and was undertaking a year-long training course to become a train driver. We went through the memory techniques described in this workbook and he could see the benefit they were having. After a coffee break he told me, 'I'm convinced the techniques work and I can see that they work. But part of me is holding back. My brain is saying, "Stick with what you know because that's the way you've always learnt".'

There was a conflict for him between the hard evidence and his feelings.

In the same way, the memory techniques in this workbook may be unfamiliar to you to start with. They might feel like new shoes in the early days – uncomfortable perhaps. So for these techniques to work, you will need to re-program how you learn. This will mean sticking at it, rather than slipping back into your old ways of learning. They may feel more comfortable but they are not as effective.

The more you use the techniques, the easier it becomes.

The rewards are likely to be plentiful, making your study time more efficient and effective. In turn, this could help improve your exam success – which is what this workbook is all about.

TOP TIP

Keep using the techniques in this book and it will get easier over time.

TOP TIP

If you want a good memory you will have to work at it.

BUILDING BLOCK 2

KNOW WHAT TYPE OF MEMORY YOU NEED

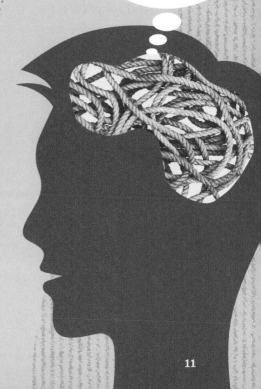

Help!! Spaghetti head!

We're going to start off with our first memory exercise. This is not about you finding out how good your memory is. Instead it's about showing you how your memory works.

Memory exercise 1

You will need
A pencil or pen
One sheet of A4 paper

Instructions
Opposite is a list of 12 words (don't look at them yet!).
They are laid out as follows:

....

Computer

....

Wallet

....

Switch

....

When you start, I want you to cover the page with the A4 sheet of paper. Then move the sheet down to reveal the first word. Read the word, then after about a second, reveal and read the next word until you have read all 12 words. Once you have exposed all the words, quickly turn the page over and write down as many of them as you can remember in the box headed 'My recall' on page 14. We will then look at how you got on.

Just to make sure you understand what you have to do, I suggest that you read these instructions again.

When you're ready, begin.

List of words to memorise

1. Plate

2. Ring

3. Spade

4. Bread

5. Cup

6. Clock

7. Bolt

8. Tree

9. Hat

10. House

11. Cake

12. Ant

Turn over immediately and write down what you remember.

?

Memory exercise 1:
My recall

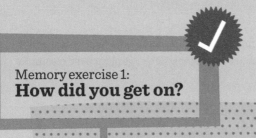

How did you get on?

Go back to the list of words you had to memorise on page 13 and tick off all those you remembered correctly. Don't worry if you haven't remembered all of the words – that's to be expected. You'll notice that the list of words has been split into three blocks, with four words in each block.

Did you recall all the words? If you did, that's good going. Most people forget at least some of the words.

Did you recall more of the words in the first block compared to the middle block? If you did, then that's similar to what we often find. We'll explore this a little later.

Did you recall more of the words in the last block compared to the middle block? If you did, this is again quite common.

Did you forget more of the words in the middle block when compared to the first and last block? Again, this is a common finding.

If your recall didn't fit the pattern above, then don't worry about it. We're all different. Read on to discover what I've found out in general.

I have been using this memory exercise for a number of years with trainees when I coach them in memory techniques. Here, I've plotted the results for 30 trainees:

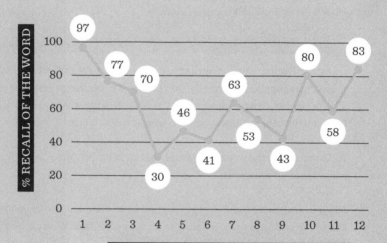

Some of the graph is a little bumpy but you will notice that recall is higher towards the beginning of the list and higher towards the end, with a dip in the middle. This is a common finding.

We could get lots of people to memorise and recall many lists of words similar to the one that you've just completed. If we then plotted all the results for all those lists on another graph we might smooth out the bumps and it may look a little like the graph opposite.

EXTRA PSYCHOLOGY FACT

Psychologists call the U shape in the graph opposite the 'serial position curve'. A researcher called Murdock was one of the first to write about this finding in 1962.

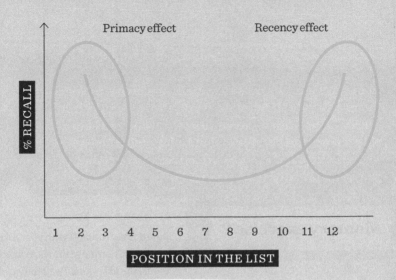

The primacy effect could be all about long-term memory

So what do psychologists think is creating this higher recall at the beginning and end of the list? The higher level of recall at the beginning is referred to as the 'primacy effect' because it is related to the primary or first words that you were presented with. Some psychologists think the higher recall here is due to these words being in the long-term memory. How do they get into long-term memory while the words in the middle don't? I often ask my trainees what they are doing with these words at the beginning of the list. They often tell me that because these words are first, and there are only a few of them, they have the opportunity to rehearse them a little more. This could lead to a stronger memory record being laid down in the long-term memory. However, once these trainees get to the middle words in the list, they are no longer able to rehearse them because they now have even more words to focus on and so the recall is lower.

The recency effect could be all about short-term memory

The higher recall at the end of the list is referred to as the 'recency' effect. This is because the words are the most recent that you remember. These have been put down in the short-term memory. As the name suggests, it is a short-term memory store. It doesn't last very long and it might also have limited capacity. So if you put new information into your short-term memory, then whatever was in there before gets displaced and drops out. Add in even more information and again whatever was in there gets shunted out, and so on.

Here's 'Memory exercise 2' which shows what happens to our 'recency effect' when we try to displace the last words in the list with something else. This will help us to understand how we should study and when we should study. The exercise is similar to the first but with a little maths test in the middle.

Memory exercise 2

You will need
A pencil or pen
One sheet of A4 paper

Instructions
On the next page is another list of 12 words – again don't look at them yet! The words are laid out as before, ie:

....

Computer

....

Wallet

....

Switch

....

Again cover the page with your A4 sheet of paper. Then move the sheet down to reveal the first word. Read the word, then after about a second, reveal and read the next word until you have read all 12 words. Once you have exposed all the words, immediately turn over the page and complete the maths test, which will be simple arithmetic, ie:

$12 + 32 =$ ☐

Write your answers in the spaces provided and work through the maths problems as quickly as you can. Focus on the maths test and not on trying to remember or rehearse the words. Once you've completed all the questions, you'll then have the opportunity to remember the words in the list. Finally we'll see how you got on.

Just to make sure you understand what you have to do, I suggest you read these instructions again.

Memory exercise 2:
List of words to memorise

1. Shop

2. Bat

3. Watch

4. Coin

5. Car

6. Bell

7. Cat

8. Brick

9. Shoe

10. Spoon

11. Desk

12. Bird

Now turn over immediately for the maths test.

Memory exercise 2:
Maths test

21 + 16 = ... 18 + 11 = ...

15 + 12 = ... 20 + 18 = ...

48 – 9 = ... 29 – 3 = ...

50 / 5 = ... 16 + 82 = ...

15 + 27 = ... 22 + 17 = ...

17 + 15 = ... 34 + 13 = ...

22 + 26 = ... 18 + 14 = ...

13 + 14 = ... 103 + 18 = ...

46 – 9 = ... 24 – 3 = ...

Write down as many of the words as you can remember.

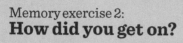

Memory exercise 2:
How did you get on?

As with exercise 1, tick off on page 21 all the words that you remembered correctly. You will notice again that the list of words has been split into three blocks, with four words in each block.

- Did you recall all the words?
- Did you recall more of the words in the first block at the beginning of the list, when compared to the other two blocks?
- Did you recall more of the words in the last block or has the recency effect disappeared?

I have plotted the results of this exercise from my group of trainees below.

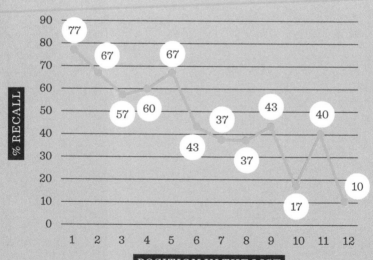

POSITION IN THE LIST

Based on 30 people

There is a still a primacy effect, with people remembering more of the first few words. This is probably because they are rehearsing them, but even with rehearsal the recall of these words is not 100%.

However, the big change in the graph is that the higher recall that was at the end of the previous list has disappeared. The recency effect has gone – whatever was in the short-term memory has disappeared!

TOP TIP

Ditch rote rehearsal (repeating information over and over) as a memory technique.

Long-term memory is best for exam success

So we are saying there are two types of memory – long-term and short-term. If we want to remember lots of information in an exam, then we need to focus on improving our long-term memory and not our short-term memory. It would be unwise to use our short-term memory by cramming it with lots of information minutes before we go into an exam, hoping what we have learnt is relevant! So developing our long-term memory is what we will work on and that is our focus for this workbook.

TOP TIP

Once you've learnt something have a break before testing yourself on it – the longer, the better. Then you will be testing what is in your long-term memory.

BUILDING BLOCK 3

UNDERSTAND IT TO MEMORISE IT

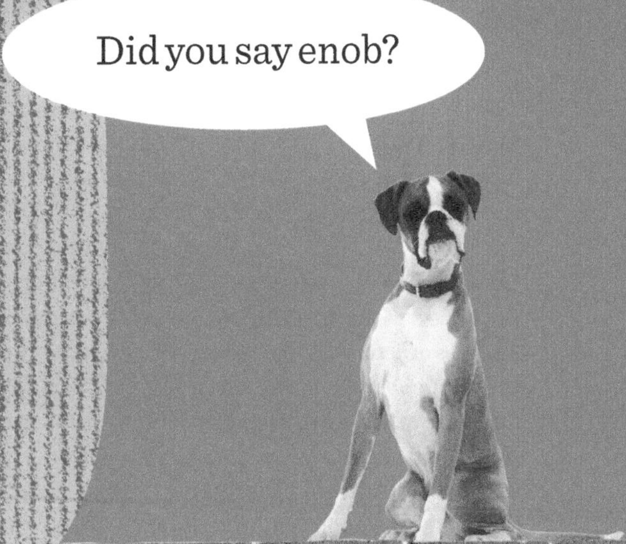

You're sitting in your classroom or lecture theatre and your teacher is explaining something very complex that you need to understand for your exams. You have no idea what they are talking about and are struggling to 'get it'. What do you do? Do you come away from the teaching session and try again to understand it or resign yourself to the fact that you'll never get it instead having to learn it parrot fashion to get you through the exam?

This building block is about exploring what impact your understanding will have on your memory.

Memory exercise 3

You will need
A pencil or pen
A timer

Instructions
On the next page you will find three passages of fictitious information. All of them are about communication that, let's say, you are revising for your Media Studies exam. I want you to read and learn each of them, one at a time, spending a minute on each. (Use the timer for this.) When you're reading one passage, try not to have a sneak preview of the ones that follow, and avoid rehearsing a previous passage in your head when you should be learning the current one!

At the end of the third passage there will be another maths test for you to complete immediately. Write your answers in the spaces provided. The maths test will clear any information that is stored in your short-term memory. This will allow us to test what is in your long-term memory.

After the maths test you will then have three questions to answer for each passage. Answer the questions from memory without going back to the original passages. Write your answers in the spaces provided. We'll then look at how much you've remembered.

If you're not sure about these instructions, then read them again.

Passage 1

The OCDS (Office Control Dialogue System) allows the mechanical and electrical control systems in large offices to dialogue with external communication sources. It also provides a platform for developing new processes for integrating existing control systems with other prevalent office processes. These could be processes within TPX, human resources, finance, and manufacturing. New applications in dialogue for OCDS include the development of PRISCODNC feathering when used with multimodal channels.

Passage 2

Technical books, trade journals and technical publications are used as communication materials, and are produced on a regular basis, eg weekly, monthly or bimonthly. This communication can include hard and soft versions, eg printed books or web-based articles. The communication provides information about developments and research in engineering, science and manufacturing. They are usually designed for specific industries.

Passage 3

If you are communicating to a colleague by telephone, then you need to make sure that you speak clearly and slowly. If you are spelling out a word, then you must use the phonetic alphabet, eg A – Alpha, B – Bravo etc. If you do not understand what you have been told, then ask for the information to be repeated. Once you have finished communicating, you need to make a log of the conversation in the daily log book.

Memory exercise 3:
Maths test

20 + 15 =   17 + 13 =

16 + 11 =   10 + 19 =

47 – 8 =   29 – 3 =

70 / 5 =   15 + 84 =

17 + 26 =   20 + 13 =

16 + 13 =   12 + 14 =

24 + 13 =   12 – 7 =

59 – 18 =   40 – 14 =

80 / 8 =   19 + 84 =

13 + 28 =   33 - 24 =

How much can you remember?

Write down your answers to the following questions from memory:

Passage 1

1. What is TPX?
2. Fill in the missing words: 'New applications in dialogue for OCDS include the development of _____ when used with multimodal channels.'
3. What can be dialogued with external communication sources?

Passage 2

1. How regularly are these communication materials produced?
2. Fill in the missing words: 'The communication provides information about developments and research in engineering, science and _____'.
3. Who are these communication materials usually designed for?

Passage 3

1. What is 'B' in the phonetic alphabet?
2. Fill in the missing words: 'If you are communicating to a colleague by telephone, then you need to make sure that you speak clearly and _____'.
3. What do you need to do if you do not understand what you have been told?

Memory exercise 3:
The correct answers

Passage 1

1. It is an office process that can be integrated with existing control systems
2. PRISCODNC feathering
3. Mechanical and electrical control systems

Your score

Passage 2

1. Weekly, monthly or bimonthly (you only need one of these to get a mark)
2. Manufacturing
3. Specific industries

Your score

Passage 3

1. Bravo
2. Slowly
3. Ask for the information to be repeated

Your score

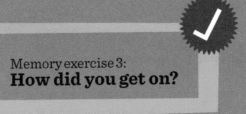
Which passage did you find most difficult to remember information from? Which passage did you find the easiest? There is a good chance that your recall fits one of the following patterns:

Highest recall in order	Highest recall in order	Highest recall in order
1. Passage 3	1. Passage 3	1. Passage 3
2. Passage 2	2. Passage 1	2. Passage 2 and 1
3. Passage 1	3. Passage 2	have equal recall

I use a similar exercise with my trainees, but I vary the passages and each group of people is different. However, it is always the case that passage 3 has the highest recall. Most of the time passage 2 has the next highest recall with passage 1 having the lowest. The average recall is shown in the graph below:

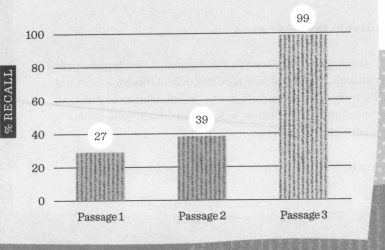

Easier to understand – easier to remember

So why do you think passage 1 is the hardest to remember, whilst passage 3 is the easiest? I ask my trainees a similar question and sometimes they'll say that they couldn't relate to passages 1 or 2. However, the most common response is that they couldn't *understand* passage 1. Passage 2 was still quite hard to understand, but passage 3 was easily understood. This is very important and the reason I set up this exercise. If you understand what you are trying to learn, then you will find it easier to learn and you will remember it better.

EXTRA PSYCHOLOGY FACT

This relates to the memory work of two psychologists Craik and Lockhart who, back in 1972, suggested that the deeper you process what you are trying to learn, the higher the recall.

A simple way to illustrate this is to look at the following example. I might ask you to learn three lists of letters for me. The first consists of random letters:

List 1: l l o e n t s a g d h t e a w t o h

I could give you a minute to learn these letters and you would probably find it very difficult. They're just individual letters, it's difficult to extract any meaning from them and you can't process the information to a deep level. What's more, there are 18 of them, which is a lot to learn in one minute. So your recall is likely to be very low.

However, let me take the same letters and arrange them into words:

List 2: Wall dog the on the sat

There's a good chance you'll find it easier to learn these same letters as they're now arranged as words. Words are much easier to understand than random letters and you can process them to a deeper level. Also, there are only six of them to remember. So if you have one minute to learn these, your recall is likely to be higher than for List 1.

Finally, let's now take the same words and rearrange them into a sentence:

List 3: The dog sat on the wall

This is now easy to learn. I can extract full meaning from the words. The random words have now been arranged as a sentence. I fully understand the sentence. I can process it to a deep level and it will help me have higher recall.

TOP TIP

When studying for an exam, make sure you fully understand what you are learning before committing it to memory.

How to get the understanding you need

Your lecturer or teacher might be explaining something to you that you don't understand. Or you might be studying your Geography text book and come across the following passage:

Soil profiles

A vertical cross section of the soil provides a number of different horizons. The highest level is the leaf litter level. Underneath this is the fermentation layer. The lowest level is the bedrock. Above this is the regolith, unlike the second level which is the topsoil. The regolith is the weathered parent material. The subsoil is in between and includes possible iron and clay accumulation. Above this is organic material and possibly calcium carbonates with a process of translocation operating here.

This is quite difficult to get your head around but you would need to understand it if you want to do well in your Geography exam. If you just learn it parrot fashion and are asked a question about what impact translocation has on the soil profile in your exam, the chances are you won't know the answer. So what do you do? If there's anything you don't understand at school or college, then seek out help. Be courageous and ask your teacher/ lecturer during or after the lesson or lecture. Getting understanding can sometimes mean asking lots of questions but it's OK to do that. You could ask a trusted friend for their explanation. Can they explain it in a different way that will help you? This might take some time and effort but it will be so much easier to learn once you 'get it'.

BUILDING BLOCK 4

MAKE IT DISTINCTIVE AND BIZARRE

Me? Bizarre? Grrrr. Roarr!

Memory exercise 4

You will need
A pencil or pen
One sheet of A4 paper

Instructions
On the next page is another list of 10 words – don't look at them yet. The words are laid out as before, ie:

....

Car

....

Sticker

....

Phone

....

Cover the page with your A4 sheet of paper, then move it down to expose the first word. Read the word, then after about a second, reveal and read the next word until you have read all 10 words. Once you have exposed all the words, as quickly as you can, turn over the page. There is another maths test for you to complete with simple arithmetic, ie:

$12 + 32 =$ ⬚

Write your answers in the spaces provided and work as quickly as you can. Focus on the maths test and not on trying to remember or rehearse the words. Once you have completed all the maths problems, look at the next page where you will have the opportunity to write down the words you remember from the list.

To make sure you understand what you have to do, I suggest you read these instructions again.

Memory exercise 4:
List of words to memorise

1. Cat

2. Shoe

3. Gate

4. Door

5. Pen

6. Chitty Chitty Bang Bang

7. Bag

8. Dog

9. Tap

10. Desk

Now complete the maths test below.

22 + 15 =	17 + 13 =
14 + 11 =	21 + 17 =
57 − 9 =	28 − 2 =
42 / 3 =	15 + 83 =
14 + 28 =	21 + 18 =
16 + 14 =	15 + 12 =
20 + 18 =	15 − 8 =
59 − 9 =	20 − 16 =
60 / 10 =	17 + 93 =
15 + 29 =	32 + 76 =

Write down as many words from the list as you can remember.

....

....

....

....

....

....

....

....

....

....

Now make a note of the number of words you recalled in the blue box on page 50.

How did you get on?

There is a good chance that you have remembered some but not all of the words. However, I would predict that you did remember 'Chitty Chitty Bang Bang'.

I use this same exercise when I'm coaching trainees in memory techniques. Everyone remembers 'Chitty Chitty Bang Bang'. However, there is never perfect recall of the other words. Look at the graph below.

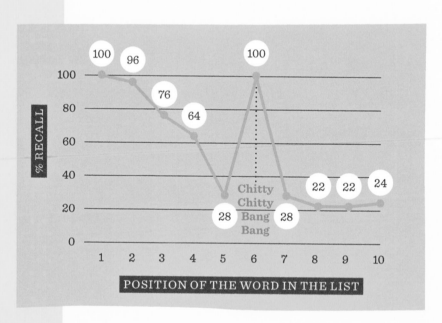

You can see that we have a nice primacy effect at the beginning of the list of words, but then the recall drops off rapidly. Then it spikes at 'Chitty Chitty Bang Bang' with 100% recall – everyone remembers it. But the average recall of all the other nine words together is only 51%. So, the recall for 'Chitty Chitty Bang Bang' is twice as high as all the other words.

The big question is why? Why do you think people remember 'Chitty Chitty Bang Bang' but forget some of the other words? When I ask my trainees this question, they tell me it's because it stands out from all the others. It is distinctive and different. It is not one word but four. When I use this experiment in my training, I read the words out loud and I shout out 'Chitty Chitty Bang Bang'. This makes it even more distinctive and sometimes shocks my trainees! For you, it was written in a big, red font.

TOP TIP

If what you are trying to learn is distinctive and bizarre, it will be easier to memorise and recall.

Distinctive memories stand out from the crowd

So what do we learn from this exercise? In our day-to-day lives we are more likely to remember events that stand out from all the others. So, if I asked you to remember what you were doing on 29 September last year, you might find it difficult to remember the day – unless it is a day that stands out for you. However, if I asked you what you did on your last birthday, or Christmas Day, or another religious festival or national holiday, then you might remember it. This is because those memories stand out. Other distinctive memories are those where something happens for the first time. So I can remember the first girl I kissed, the first time I drove a car on my own, what I was doing on 9/11, my first lecture, the birth of my son and my first day at school.

Why are we more likely to remember distinctive memories?

It could be that when we are trying to remember something, we consciously trawl through a whole range of similar memories to find the memory we're looking for. Supposing we were trying to remember what we did on a particular day last year. Many of these days would be quite similar, so it would be hard to distinguish between them and find the right memory.

It's like me giving you a giant box of Smarties® and you having to find the one I've marked with a very small spot on it. It will be difficult and frustrating to find. Every Smartie that you look at could be the one you're looking for. All those other Smarties® are hindering your search for the right one. If you have patience and diligence, you will probably find it. But what a job!

Let's say instead that I make one Smartie distinctive and put it in the box with the others. This time it's 20 times bigger than all the others and is bright orange. When you look for it this time, you will probably find it immediately. So the same goes for searching memories. If all the memories are similar they interfere with each other. If one is distinctive it's easier to recall, because it stands out.

TOP TIP

If you make what you want to learn distinctive, then it will stand out from all the other memories and it will be easier to recall.

EXTRA PSYCHOLOGY FACT

Interference theory is one way psychologists explain the process of forgetting. A good online summary of it by Saul McLeod is available at
http://www.simplypsychology.org/forgetting.html

Work at making learning material distinctive

To make what you have to learn distinctive, you will need to work at it. Most of what you're trying to learn for your exams is likely to be lacking distinctiveness. It may not be particularly interesting; it could be quite bland and boring. So you need to work on the information to make it stand out in your memory.

One way of doing this is to think of the information in a bizarre or humorous way. You will need to let your creative juices flow and your imagination run riot. Some people find this quite unnatural and have to work at it. Others take to it like a duck to water. However, the more you practise, the easier it will get.

The best way for you to understand how this works is for me to give you an example. Let's say I need to learn the words 'cat' and 'pen'. Here is how I might let my imagination run riot to make the words distinctive so they will stand out in my memory:

WORD TO LEARN	MAKING IT DISTINCTIVE	MY IMAGE
Cat	I am thinking of an enormous cat that is 100 times bigger than me, licking my face with her gigantic, wet, sloppy tongue, purring very loudly. The cat has really bad breath too and it makes me wince with disgust.	
Pen	I am thinking of being rained on by thousands of different coloured pens. The pens don't have tops and as they hit me, they mark the white suit I'm wearing and my hands/face with different colours.	

Have a go at making it distinctive

Let's have a go at a simple exercise, so that you can for you to see for yourself the positive effect on your recall of making what you have to learn distinctive and bizarre. Before we do, though, go back to 'Memory exercise 4' on page 39, and note the total number of words you remembered. Now go forward to page 50 and write the number in the blue box. We'll look at this later.

You will have another list of 10 words. However, in this exercise when you are learning each word, I want you to work on it. Make it distinctive and bizarre – make it stand out. Use your imagination, make it funny and try to play with the word in some way.

Dog breath? How very dare you!

Memory exercise 5

You will need
A pencil or pen
One sheet of A4 paper

Instructions
On the next page is a list of 10 words.
Again don't look at them yet!

Cover the page with your A4 sheet of paper, then, move the sheet down to reveal the first word.

Read the word, then spend a couple of seconds turning the word into something that is bizarre, distinctive and humorous. Then reveal the next word and do the same again until you have read all 10 words. Once you've revealed all the words, as quickly as you can, turn over for your maths test. This is identical to the other maths tasks, ie:

$12 + 32 =$

Write your answers in the spaces provided. Again focus on the maths test and try not to remember or rehearse the words. Once it's completed you can then write down the words you remember.

List of words to memorise

1. Toe

2. Egg

3. Glass

4. Mouse

5. House

6. Book

7. Swan

8. Pig

9. Sock

10. Badge

Now complete the maths test below.

$32 + 12 =$ $27 + 14 =$

$34 + 51 =$ $20 + 18 =$

$58 - 7 =$ $26 - 5 =$

$40 / 4 =$ $16 + 85 =$

$13 + 29 =$ $22 + 19 =$

$15 + 13 =$ $14 + 13 =$

$21 + 17 =$ $14 - 7 =$

$58 - 8 =$ $21 - 15 =$

$70 / 10 =$ $18 + 95 =$

$16 + 30 =$ $32 + 47 =$

?

Write down as many of the words from the list you can remember.

....

....

....

....

....

....

....

....

....

....

....

....

Memory exercise 5:
How did you get on?

Go back to the list of words you had to learn on page 47 and and see how many you've remembered correctly.

Now write in the red box below the number of words you recalled. You should have already completed the other blue box using your results from 'Memory Exercise 4'.

The total number of words that I recalled in exercise 4

The total number of words that I recalled in exercise 5

Hopefully your recall has improved.

I use similar exercises in my workshops and these are the results that I've found:

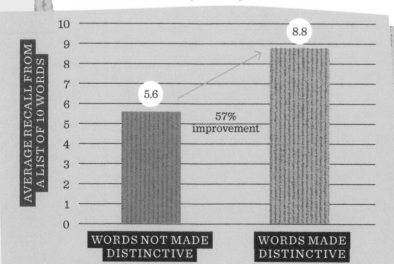

You can see that when trainees changed their style of learning by making the words distinctive, their recall rose by a staggering 57%. What this shows us is that when you work on the information you have to learn and make it distinctive, bizarre and humorous, then your recall improves.

Let's take one more example to demonstrate how this works. I need to learn the following information for a history exam. The chart overleaf shows how I would make things distinctive, bizarre and humorous. Of course, you would probably come up with an entirely different set of images

Ancient Greek medicine

There were lots of wars the Ancient Greeks were involved in. This meant they became experts at first aid. If a patient had a back problem, eg a slipped disc, then they would try to cure it by another warrior standing on his back. They also knew about curing a broken bone.

WHAT I AM TRYING TO REMEMBER	MY DISTINCTIVE, BIZARRE, AND HUMOROUS IMAGE
There were lots of wars the Ancient Greeks were involved in. This meant they became experts at first aid.	I imagine an army of Ancient Greek soldiers marching forward wearing white suits with a red cross on their forehead, all carrying syringes the size of spears.
If a patient had a back problem, eg a slipped disc, then they would try to cure it by other warriors standing on his back.	At the back of the army I imagine a line of Greek soldiers jumping 20 feet in the air, saying a loud 'Wheeee!' and then landing on the back of another Greek soldier. Every time a soldier lands on his poorly back, he gives out an enormous 'Ouch!'.
They also knew about curing a broken bone.	At the front of the army there is a whole line of soldiers who have their entire bodies covered in plaster and they're marching on crutches. Every time they walk forward, they fall over.

Wheeee!

Ouch! Was that really necessary?

Notice that I try to use sound and humour to enrich what I need to learn. And I have tried to combine all the things I need to learn into one interactive image. This is something we will return to later in this workbook.

Now it's your turn

Take something you currently need to learn and try making it bizarre, distinctive and humorous. It may require some effort so take a small chunk of information to start with. If you find this technique works for you, keep practising!

BUILDING BLOCK 5

USE IMAGES

I only asked for a trim!!

This building block touches on what we covered in 'Building block 4' but I think it's important enough for it to have its own section. It is all about the impact imagery can have on your recall. As before, we start with an exercise.

Memory exercise 6

You will need
A pencil or pen
One sheet of A4 paper

Instructions
On the next page is a list of 16 words. Don't look at them yet!

Cover the page with your A4 sheet of paper, then move the sheet down to expose the first word. Let's say the words you have to learn are for your NVQ Childcare Certificate and are the 16 words that are the least common an 8-year-old would utter – completely fictitious, of course!

Try to commit the words to memory but avoid using any of the memory techniques you have already learnt in this workbook. This will help illustrate the effect more strongly. Give yourself a second to learn each word. Then expose the next word and so on until you have read and studied all 16 words.

Once you have exposed all the words, as quickly as you can, turn over for your maths test. This is identical to the other maths tasks. Again put your efforts into the maths test and try not to remember or rehearse the words. Once the maths test is complete, you can then write down the words you remember.

1. Tile

2. Detail

3. Drum

4. New

5. Pram

6. Rare

7. Pipe

8. Mend

9. Brush

10. Rank

11. Flag

12. Low

13. Star

14. Fast

15. Tree

16. Make

Memory exercise 6:
Maths test

Now complete the maths test below.

42 + 22 =   37 + 18 =

36 + 50 =   25 + 19 =

78 – 9 =   106 – 5 =

50 / 5 =   19 + 88 =

15 + 25 =   27 + 12 =

16 + 18 =   16 + 19 =

25 + 19 =   19 – 7 =

89 – 8 =   25 – 19 =

90 / 10 =   28 + 105 =

36 + 52 =   32 + 976 =

Write down as many words from the list as you can.

Go back to the list of words you had to learn on page 55 and tick off those you recalled correctly.

Now work out the following two scores and write them in the boxes:

The total amount of words recalled that were numbered with an odd number, ie words numbered 1, 3, 5, 7 etc

The total amount of words recalled that were numbered with an even number, ie words numbered 2, 4, 6, 8 etc

You may have found that you recalled more of the odd numbered words than the even numbered words.

More imagery = higher recall

Why do you think you might have learnt more of the odd words than the even words? Go back and have a look at the odd and even words in the list and see what the difference might be. You may have noticed that the odd words were all words that are objects, and so are easy to imagine. We call these 'high imagery words'. In contrast, the even words are all non-object words, describing words or doing words. They are difficult to imagine. We call these 'low imagery words'.

EXTRA PSYCHOLOGY FACT

Researchers such as RN Shepard back in the late 1960s and early 70s were able to demonstrate our extraordinary memory for images. See the reference on page 104 for more information.

Words with lots of imagery are rich in information

So what is it about the high imagery words that means we remember them better? As the saying goes, 'A picture paints a thousand words'. An image can be very rich with information and colour, and so probably aids our recall. Also images can be quite distinctive – we already know this helps our memory. For example, if I think about the car that I drive – a red Mini, the image is very distinctive.

If we blend this building block with the previous one by making the image bizarre and distinctive, then it could aid our memory still further. You can now appreciate that in my Ancient Greek history scenario on pages 51 and 52, I was using both imagery and distinctiveness to help aid recall.

Learning new words, ideas or concepts

When you are studying, you might have to learn new words, ideas and concepts that you have never come across before. So they may be difficult to learn and commit to memory. On the next page are some examples, with suggestions of how I might go about remembering them.

TOP TIP

Create an image in your mind of what you are trying to learn. This will help you to remember it.

SUBJECT AREA	WHAT I HAVE TO MEMORISE	MY IMAGE
French	*La foule*	La foule, which means the crowd, is pronounced 'fool'. So I imagine a large crowd of people watching a football match when a football player with a big 'E' on his head then fouls another player. This will help me remember the spelling, foul-e. The crowd shout and scream 'Fool' at the player who is fouling the other. This will help me remember the pronunciation.
Geology	*Afrovenator* – the name of a dinosaur from the mid-Jurassic period	I imagine a dinosaur with an afro hairstyle (this will help me remember Afro) with the letters VE on tiny placards coming out of his hair. (This will help me remember VE). Then on the ends of the placards there are military aeroplanes flying around with NATO on their wings. (This will help me remember NATO.) Finally the dinosaur is watching *Jurassic Park* on TV. (This will help me remember Jurassic period.) The film is only showing in the middle part of the TV. (This will help me remember mid-Jurassic period.)

Well, at least I haven't lost my dignity

A GOOD SET OF KEYS HELPS TO UNLOCK YOUR MEMORIES

The first half of this workbook has given you five building blocks that can help improve your memory.

The second half of this workbook now focuses on some very specific memory techniques that can unlock your memories for you – it's all about keys and locks.

When you can't remember...

If you try to remember some important study material and you find you can't remember it, then you might quite rightly conclude you've forgotten it. However, it might be the case that it is still stored in your memory but you have lost access to it. If you were given the right set of keys then it might unlock the memory for you. So, as before, let's start off with a memory exercise.

Memory exercise 7

You will need
Two pencils or pens of different colours
One sheet of A4 paper

Instructions
On the next page is a list of 20 paired words. They are presented as follows:

Ball   Bat

The word on the right is the target word that you are trying to memorise and the word on the left is the cue, ie:

Cue   **Target**
Ball   Bat

Let's say this is a list of the objects a fictitious medieval artist, Crescendo, painted. You need to learn all of these 20 objects for your History of Art exam. Once you've learnt them, you will have another maths task to complete. You will then write down the target words you've remembered in two different ways:

1.   **Free recall:** Remember as many of the 20 target words on the right-hand side as you can without any help and without any of the cue words. You will need to cover the cued recall test on page 67.

2.   **Cued recall:** Here we will help you by giving you the cue word on the left-hand side, and you will then have to recall the target word that went with it.

It's very important that you learn the target word and you link it to its cue word. For this exercise to work you really need to understand these instructions. So I recommend that you read them again – just to make sure.

There is one pair of words on each line. Cover them with your A4 sheet of paper, then move it down to expose the first pair of words. When you're learning each pair, try to avoid using the memory techniques you've already learnt. Instead, just try to associate each pair of words – give yourself 2 or 3 seconds to do this. Then expose the next pair, and so on, until you have read and studied all 20 pairs.

Once you have exposed all the pairs, as quickly as you can, do the maths test on the next page. Again focus on the maths test and try not to remember or rehearse the cue words or the word pairs. Once the maths test is completed, turn over and complete the two recall tasks – free recall and cued recall.

List of words to memorise

	Cue	Target		Cue	Target
1.	Bread	Knife	11.	Tea	Milk
2.	Mouse	Cat	12.	Tree	Branch
3.	Spoon	Cup	13.	Tap	Sink
4.	Cloud	Sun	14.	Rail	Train
5.	Beef	Grass	15.	Horse	Hay
6.	Frame	Paint	16.	Pen	Card
7.	Hand	Ring	17.	Bolt	Screw
8.	Clock	Hand	18.	Salt	Meal
9.	Stamp	Card	19.	Key	Door
10.	Seed	Pot	20.	Robe	Queen

Now complete the maths test.

43 + 25 =	57 + 28 =
56 + 40 =	35 + 29 =
88 – 19 =	116 – 15 =
80 / 5 =	39 + 88 =
35 + 25 =	57 + 12 =
36 + 18 =	16 + 59 =
55 + 39 =	67 – 19 =
79 – 13 =	28 – 15 =
130 / 10 =	48 + 115 =
56 + 52 =	34 + 32 =

Cover the cued recall exercise words opposite.

Write here as many of the 20 target words as you can remember. These were the words on the right-hand side of the two lists.

....

....

....

....

....

....

....

....

....

....

....

You have just written down as many of the target words as you could remember. This would suggest that you have forgotten all the other objects that Crescendo painted. However, let's see what happens when we now give you the cue for each of the target words. Move onto the next page for your cued recall.

Here are the cue words for each pair. Write down as many target words as you can remember next to each one.

Cue	Target	Cue	Target
1. Bread		11. Tea	
2. Mouse		12. Tree	
3. Spoon		13. Tap	
4. Cloud		14. Rail	
5. Beef		15. Horse	
6. Frame		16. Pen	
7. Hand		17. Bolt	
8. Clock		18. Salt	
9. Stamp		19. Key	
10. Seed		20. Robe	

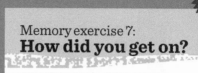

Free recall: Go back to the list of paired words you had to learn on page 64 and tick off with one coloured pen/pencil those target words you remembered correctly. From your answers on page 66 add up the total and put the number in this box:

Cued recall: Go back to the list of paired words you learnt on page 64 and, using your second coloured pen/pencil, tick off those target words you recalled correctly with the *right target cue word*. From your answers on page 67 add up the total and put the number in this box:

Hopefully you remembered some of the words with free recall but there's a good chance you forgot some of them. You might have concluded that only the target words you remembered were in your memory and you had therefore forgotten all the other words.

However, I would predict that you were able to remember more of the target words when you were given their cues. These extra target words were in your memory but you had just lost access to them. We could say you lost the keys to unlock the memories. When we gave you a set of keys (the cued words), it unlocked more of the target words.

I use a similar exercise with trainees to show the impact of giving a set of keys to remember a list of words, and this is what I've found.

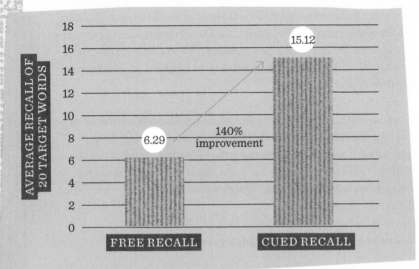

The chart shows that trainees just couldn't get access to some memories under free recall. But once they were given the right cues, their recall rose dramatically (by 140%).

TOP TIP

Just because you can't remember something doesn't necessarily mean you have forgotten it.

Memory cues in day-to-day life

In the UK after a major crime the police will often undertake a reconstruction to help jog people's memories. This can help existing witnesses to remember more about the incident: 'Yes, now I remember a young man running across the road at the same time'. It could also help those who didn't think they were witnesses to realise they did see something on the day of the crime: 'Yes, I was there, and I do remember a red van speeding quickly through the village at 12.30. I thought it was a little odd but forgot about it'. What the police are doing is using the reconstruction as a set of keys to help people remember.

We often use this technique with our family and friends when we remember an event and they can't. We'll often try to help them by saying, 'Don't you remember? It was on the day that you couldn't get your mobile to work and while you were trying to sort it out, you dropped ice cream all down your front and we burst out laughing'. Again we give cues to act as keys to unlock the memories.

You need a good set of keys to help you remember

So to help us remember more, we need a good set of keys that are easy to use and will help us unlock the memories. In fact, we need a set of keys that will be easy to remember themselves! For these keys to work, we need to make a strong link or association between the key and what we are trying to remember. If we don't, the keys will be next to useless and they won't necessarily unlock the right memories.

The next few techniques are all about giving you different sets of keys that are easy to use and will help unlock what you are trying to remember. You may find some of the key sets better than others. Some may work for you, others may not. But once you've learnt what they are and how to use them, you can choose what works best for you.

KEY AND LOCK 1

LOCATION

The first key and lock is known as the 'method of loci'. This just means that you use a physical location which is very familiar to us, and make a strong link between the location and what we are trying to learn. Good places to choose might be your home, your school, your best friend's house, your university campus or your place of work. A very familiar location is easy to remember and so it has the potential to be a good set of keys.

Worked example for the method of loci

Here's a worked example of mine so that you get the idea.

I am sitting my Physical Education exam and I have to remember the seven items that make up a balanced diet. They are:

- Vitamins
- Carbohydrates
- Fibre
- Minerals
- Water
- Protein
- Fats

TOP TIP

Using the method of loci technique is especially useful if you are trying to remember things in a particular order.

The physical location I've used as my set of keys to remember this list is my own house. I imagine walking through the front door and then walking up the stairs and into different rooms. I associate each item on the list with a part of my house like this:

EXTRA PSYCHOLOGY FACT

The method of loci dates back to the Ancient Romans and Greeks. To learn more about the history of the technique, go to http://en.wikipedia.org/wiki/Method_of_loci.

As I push open the front door, I imagine thousands of vitamin pills as high as the door, pouring out onto the floor. This will help me remember 'vitamins'.

I then wade through the vitamin pills and go up the stairs. I am tripped up by massive potatoes and pasta shapes falling down towards me. This will help me remember 'carbohydrates'.

I pick myself up. At the top of the stairs I turn left and the hallway is covered from ceiling to floor in tiny fibre optics that are blocking my way – they are like spaghetti. This will help me remember 'fibre'.

I wade through the fibres and I open our bedroom door. As I open the door, a large box of stones that are perched on the top of the door fall on my head. It hurts and I go 'Ouch!'. This will help me remember 'minerals'.

I'm way too small for this wave!

I rub my head until it stops hurting and I turn to go into the en-suite bathroom. As I open the door, I am washed out of the bathroom on a tide of water, with my wife surfing it on a board. This will help me remember 'water'.

I am drenched and I pick myself up, turn around and step over the stones from the box. I then turn right and my study door is blocked by large containers of protein powder mix, used by weight trainers. The containers are stacked floor to ceiling. I punch the containers and they fall down. This will help me remember 'protein'.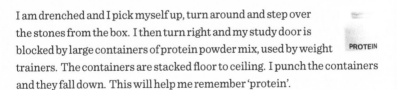

I open the door into my study, where my 5-year-old son is sitting at my desk eating chips about one metre in length and rashers of bacon that are two metres in length. They are all dripping in fat. With a mouth full of food he shouts, 'Hello daddy! I'm eating fatty food'. This will help me remember 'fats'.

That is the technique! The images and story work for me. They are personal and will help me to remember those seven key items that make up a balanced diet. If you were trying to learn these same items, then you would need your own location and your own images and story.

A memorable set of keys

You may have spotted from my example that I have included some of the other techniques you've already learnt in this workbook: 'Building block 5', using imagery, and 'Building block 4', making the imagery bizarre and distinctive. Using a number of building blocks will greatly increase your ability to remember because it strengthens the link between the key and the lock.

Another great thing about the method of loci is that you can start at any point in your chosen location and work backwards or forwards to remember information. So, taking my example above, I may not be able to remember the key to unlock the word 'protein'. But if I remember how my study is linked to the word 'fats', I can imagine walking back through my study to the door which can unlock the memory for me.

Now try it for yourself

You are also revising for your Physical Education exam. You have to remember all those things that could affect your performance in sport. They are:

– Drugs
– Diet
– Personal cleanliness
– Age
– Psychological factors
– Technology

TOP TIP

Use a familiar physical location as your set of keys to link with what you are trying to remember.

Now use the method of loci to remember this list. Use a location that is familiar to you. Use imagery. Make those images distinctive and bizarre and try to interact with them in some way. Once you feel you have learnt all seven items, then go back and test yourself. If you are unable to remember a particular item, then go back and work on it again. Make the image more distinctive and link it to the location or room.

KEY AND LOCK 2

NUMBERS

Seven swans a swimming?... Nope, can't remember the rest.

Most of us will find it easy to recall numbers in consecutive order. It is something that we learnt when we were very young. So given that numbers are so easy to remember, they should work well as another set of keys. We just need to find a strong link between the key (the numbers) and the lock (what we are trying to remember).

There are two ways that we can use numbers to help us learn.

1. Using numbers and rhyme

With this technique we use words that rhyme with numbers to help create an image. Once we have an image, we can then use this key to link it to what we are trying to learn. Here's an example to show you what I mean.

I am revising for my Business Studies exam and I have to remember all the different recruitment tools an employer might use. These are:

1. Application form
2. Interview
3. Psychometric tests
4. Role play
5. Group exercise
6. CV

First I think of a word that rhymes with 'one'. Immediately I think of 'bun'. So I now have an image. What I now have to do is link the word 'bun' with the first item on the list – 'application form'. I then imagine eating a large currant bun with an application form for Greggs the bakers rolled up tightly and sticking out of the top. The application form is lit at the top like a candle on a cake.

So what do you think you can offer our company then?

So I've now connected 'bun' with 'application form'.

Number two rhymes with 'moo'. Here I imagine a large cow sitting with glasses behind a desk interviewing me for a job. This flashes up a bizarre image for me, similar to *The Far Side* cartoons by my favourite cartoonist, Gary Larson.

So now I've connected 'moo' with 'interview'.

We can continue this with the remainder of the recruitment tools, ie:
'Three' rhymes with 'tree' so then link it with 'Psychometric tests'.
'Four' rhymes with 'door' so then link it to 'Role Play'.
'Five' rhymes with 'hive' so then link it with 'Group Exercise'.
'Six' rhymes with 'sticks' so then link it to 'CV'.

Top tips for using numbers and rhyme

- Use any words that rhyme with the numbers, but those that immediately come to mind for you when you say each number work best.
- Use rhyming words that are objects rather than words, so avoid 'mix' for 'six' or 'live' for 'five'. High imagery words are easy to recall and will be better keys to link to what you're trying to remember.
- Make the image distinctive and bizarre.

EXTRA PSYCHOLOGY FACT

It is believed that in about 1648, Stanislaus Mink von Wennsshein was one of the first to put forward the idea of using numbers as a memory technique. Visit: https://en.wikipedia.org/wiki/Stanislaus_Mink_von_Wennsshein

2. Using images of numbers

This memory technique is about using the shape of the numbers themselves to act as our keys. Again let's go through an example to show how the technique works.

I am revising for my Business Studies exam and I am studying market research techniques. The techniques that I need to learn are called 'primary research techniques', which are undertaken directly with people that companies or organisations want to market to, eg shoppers. These techniques are as follows:

1. Postal questionnaires
2. Telephone canvassing
3. Face-to-face interviews
4. Focus groups

I'm going to learn these by looking at the shape of the numbers alongside each item to see what image they create. I will then create a strong link between that image and the item I need to learn. So for example:

The number 1 looks like a walking stick to me. So this is my image and my key. I now need to link that to my first marketing technique – 'postal questionnaires'. Again I am going to use imagery to connect the two. I imagine my walking stick is made up of questionnaires that are tightly rolled up. Along the walking stick I see postage stamps. So when I think of the number 1, I think of a walking stick made up of questionnaires and the stamps remind me of the post. The link between the key and the lock has now been made.

The number 2 looks like a swan to me. I need to connect this swan to my second marketing technique – 'telephone canvassing'. The image that comes to mind is a swan on her mobile phone calling other swans. She is asking them what they think of the bread that they are fed by visitors to the lake and whether they prefer white or brown. So I have made the connection between a swan and 'telephone canvasing' and it works for me. It is also somewhat bizarre and distinctive which I know will help me remember.

The number 3 looks like a seagull flying in the sky. I imagine the seagull flying whilst interviewing other seagulls face-to-face, asking them what they think of the scenery they're travelling over. So I have connected a seagull with 'face-to-face interviews'.

The number 4 looks like a sail boat to me. I imagine a flotilla of boats, with bright sails, in the harbour arranged in a circle, with each boat having a sailor on board. There is one big boat in the middle with a big sailor on board and he is shouting loudly at the other sailors on the boats: 'I want you all to focus now and tell me what you think of the harbour here. Is it a nice place to moor your boat?' The image of the boats in a circle reminds me of a group and the sailor telling them to focus reminds me of 'focus groups'.

Croydon looks lovely today, doesn't it?

TOP TIP

Use numbers as keys to lock in the most important things you are trying to remember. The keys could be the image of each number or the image of a word that the number rhymes with.

Why the technique works

Using numbers works because they are easy to remember and we can forge strong links through imagery to what we are trying to learn. It does require some effort to create the keys and lock them into what we have to remember. But if we put in the effort up front, it can be a powerful memory technique for us. If we can make the key–lock link strong using distinctive and bizarre images, then this will be an added bonus.

Using a mobile with no arms is pretty tricky, I can tell you.

KEY AND LOCK 3

ACRONYMS

Acronyms are like abbreviations. So for example, LUL is an acronym for London Underground Limited, ASAP is an acronym for 'as soon as possible', LOL for 'laugh out loud', and so on. A more technical example might be CRT which is an acronym for cathode ray tube or MODEM – an acronym for modulator and demodulator. In our day-to-day lives, we use acronyms to communicate efficiently by creating shortcuts when we are talking, writing, tweeting or texting. For example I can write out in full:

The modulators, demodulators and cathode ray tubes at London Underground Limited are not working. Please fix as soon as possible. Lots of love Steve

Or, I might text or write the message as follows:

The MODEMs and CRTs at LUL are not working. Please fix ASAP. LoL Steve

When you think about it, an acronym is a key to unlocking another word or phrase so it's another useful memory technique and one you may have used lots in the past.

Using acronyms

Let's say I am revising for my Biology exam and I have to learn the different types of tissue:

> Muscular tissue
> Glandular tissue
> Epithelial tissue

I can rearrange these different types of tissue and create an acronym:

> Glandular tissue
> Epithelial tissue
> Muscular tissue

I now have my acroynm GEM which should help me remember the different types of tissue. If I drew a picture of a precious stone alongside the list on my study materials, then it might be an additional help:

> Glandular tissue
> Epithelial tissue
> Muscular tissue

My key is the word GEM and each letter of the word GEM should unlock the information I'm trying to remember about key tissue types. I am hoping that when I remember the letter 'E' it will act as a cue to unlock the memory 'Epithelial tissue'. However, from my experience, just relying on this letter as a cue may not always work. The link between the key and the lock is not that strong – I know the word I'm trying to remember begins with an E but that's all the information I have. However, if I combine my use of acronyms with other memory techniques, it becomes more useful.

Using acronyms with imagery

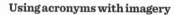

Let's see how this works. I'm revising for my Chemistry exam and I'm learning all about acids. What I have to learn is that acids:

- are corrosive when they are particularly powerful.
- are irritants when they are weak.
- have reactions with bases to create neutral chemicals.

So *corrosive*, *irritants* and *bases* are the key things I need to learn. I will rearrange these to create the acronym BIC. This reminds me of BIC pens. I will think of three BIC pens arranged in a triangle as follows:

One of these will have the letter 'B' on it – sitting on a base – this will remind me of '*base*'.

Another will have an 'I' on it being used by a hand that is itchy – this will help me remember '*irritant*'.

The third pen will have a skull and crossbones on it – this will remind me of '*corrosive*'.

So what I've done is to combine my acronym with imagery to help improve the connection between the key and the lock, thereby improving my recall. I now have two sets of keys to help unlock the same memories – one is the acronym BIC and the other is the imagery.

TOP TIP

Combine the use of acronyms with imagery to improve the connection between the key and the lock.

KEY AND LOCK 4

STORY

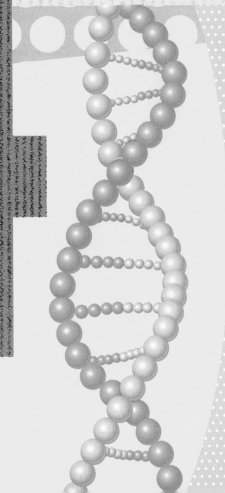

Creating a story is the next memory technique which also uses keys and locks. However, here the first key unlocks the first memory. This memory once recalled then acts as a key for the next memory and so on. So it is like a chain of keys and locks. This technique is particularly useful if you are trying to remember information in a particular order.

Once again, let's start with an example.

I am revising for my Food Technology exam and I have to remember the ethical factors that can affect consumer choice in deciding whether or not to purchase a product. These are as follows:

- *Food miles* – all about how far the food has travelled from where it was grown to where it is sold. More miles mean more carbon dioxide emissions, resulting in a negative impact on the environment.
- *Farm assured* – whoever has produced or packaged the food, ie farms or food manufacturers, has to adhere to rigorous standards around animal care, the environment and safety.
- *Fair trade* – where those who are growing the product get a fair price for their food.
- *Genetically modified* – where the genes of the food have been changed to perhaps increase yields, reduce disease or to grow in particular climates.
- *Seasonal foods* – this covers foods that are in season. It can help decrease food miles.

I am going to create a story that will try to connect all these together. It is important to note that this is my own story using what works for me, based on my own locks and keys. If you were creating your own story, then it would need to be personal to you.

1. I first think of a big lorry with 'Long distance' written on its
   side panels and a sign saying 'All the way from Australia'.
   The lorry is open-top and is packed with food. Each item has
   a label on it saying 'Miles'. This image taken together will help me to
   remember 'food miles'.

2. The lorry crashes into a big entrance sign for a large farm. The
   farm sign has 'Farm assured' written on it. This will help me
   remember 'farm assured'.

3. The lorry driver gets out of the lorry with a wad of money and
   pays the irate farmer for knocking into his farm entrance
   board. The farmer has the FAIRTRADE symbol on the front
   of his T-shirt and shakes the driver's hand and says that it's a fair price.
   This taken all together helps me remember 'fair trade'.

4. The farmer turns around and walks away. The back of his hair
   has large DNA helix curls attached to it. This will help me
   remember 'genetically modified'.

5. As the farmer walks away, the sun is very hot and the DNA
   curls start to melt and they drip on the floor. As he walks on a
   little further, it starts to rain, which stops the DNA melting.
   Taken together this helps me remember 'seasonal foods'.

That's my story. You may think it's 'off the wall' but it works for me! I have
tried to connect together the different things I have to remember, using
locks and keys in a sequential story. The lorry (food miles) is a key to unlock
the farm (farm assured). The farm is a key to unlock the farmer (fair trade).
The farmer is then a key to unlock the DNA helix (genetically modified). The
DNA helix is a key to unlock the sun and rain (seasonal foods).

'Food miles', 'farm assured', 'fair trade', 'genetically modified', and 'seasonal
foods' are all difficult terms to visualize. So I've converted each item into an
image that will act as a key to unlock the memory.

It also works backwards

As with all techniques it isn't perfect, so sometimes I'm unable to remember the next part of the story. However, if I'm able to recall some future part of the story, I can often go backwards and remember the thing I have forgotten. So let's say I have forgotten what happens after the farmer turns round, ie I forget the DNA helix. I might remember the later part of the story about the sun and rain – this then reminds me of the DNA helix melting. So I now remember 'genetically modified'. The visual image of the seasons now becomes a key to unlock an earlier memory from the story of the 'genetically modified' food. So the story can work forwards and backwards. Neat!

Your turn to create a story

Now have a go for yourself. Let's say you're revising for your History exam which is all about the impact the Second World War had on American society. Use the story technique to help you learn the list.

1. Japanese citizens were imprisoned or sent back to Japan.
2. American men were conscripted to join the army.
3. American citizens were encouraged to help the war effort by growing their own vegetables.
4. Many Americans left America to find work elsewhere.
5. Unemployment fell dramatically and many worked in factories.
6. Production from industry doubled.

As human beings we all like stories. So let's use them. You create a visual story using your imagination. The story is your set of keys that you use to lock in memories along the way. As you recall and unlock each memory, that then becomes a key for the next part of the story, and so on. It is a chain reaction. If you can make the story bizarre, distinctive and humorous too, then it will aid your recall.

TOP TIP

We all love stories. Use them to create a visual chain of keys to unlock memories.

KEY AND LOCK 5

MIND MAPS

This final memory technique is for me the most important and probably the most useful – the crème de la crème. It involves making a graphical picture of what you are trying to learn – a Mind Map, originally created by Tony Buzan. Sometimes these are referred to as spider diagrams but essentially they are the same thing.

To help show you the technique I have created a Mind Map of this workbook so far. Here it is:

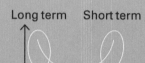

Long term   Short term

1. Work hard at it

2. Know what type of memory to work on

3. Understand what you have to learn

General building blocks

5. Use images

4. Make it funny, distinctive and bizarre

Box of Smarties®

4. ————————
5. ————————
6. Chitty Chitty Bang Bang
7. ————————
8. ————————

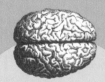

Max your memory for exam success

You need a good set of keys that fit the lock and open the memories

1. Bun – Memory
2. Moo – Memory
3. Tree – Memory
4. Door - Memory

1. Walking stick – Memory
2. Swan – Memory
3. Seagull - Memory

Rhyming with numbers

Images of numbers

1. Method of Loci

2. Numbers

Keys and locks

3. Acronyms

5. Mind maps

4. Create a story

More about the Mind Map

Let's look at some of the features of a Mind Map using the one from the previous pages:

– The description of what the Mind Map is all about is in the middle so that our eyes are drawn to it.
– Connecting lines come off the centre circle and each of these connecting lines can be divided further.
– Mind Maps just use key words and phrases as prompts. This reduces the load on our studying and learning.
– Mind Maps are visually appealing and use pictures and imagery as much as possible (Building block 5).
– I have used colour and bizarre images to help make my Mind Map distinctive. (Building block 4).
– Every Mind Map is pretty unique and personal.
– Mind Maps work best when they've been prepared on a large sheet of paper, such as A3 size.
– Mind Maps have plenty of empty space on the page so they don't look too busy.

TOP TIP

Use mind maps to help summarise a large amount of written information in a visually appealing way.

You can use Mind Maps for different purposes

I caught on to how effective Mind Maps could be during my undergraduate degree course. I used them for note-taking during lectures, studying and revision for exams, as follows:

Note-taking during lectures: I would sit in my lectures with my artist-sized sheets of paper. I would write the lecture title in the middle, eg 'Unconsciousness', and start to prepare my Mind Map as the lecturer talked. I'm sure my fellow students thought my note-taking was rather odd and I would often be the butt of good-natured jokes from my close friends. But it worked for me.

Studying: I would be in the library reading a text book or academic paper and would have my large sheet of paper next to me so I could prepare my Mind Map as I read along. Even today when I'm reading a paper or text book, I will always use Mind Maps to help me summarise and organise what I'm learning. When I'm with a business contact and they're telling me about their people issues, I will use a Mind Map to help summarise their thoughts and my ideas.

Revision for exams: Given that I was using my Mind Maps for note-taking and studying, you can imagine that I accumulated hundreds of these Mind Maps. These Mind Maps then became my revision notes for exams. I would spend many hours working through my Mind Maps, learning and testing my memory.

EXTRA PSYCHOLOGY FACT

The Mind Map technique was created and popularised by a man called Tony Buzan who is a bestselling author and international speaker. The ThinkBuzan website contains lots of advice on mind mapping, their benefits and some tools to help you create them in electronic format: visit http://thinkbuzan.com for more information

The Mind Map may not be perfect first time

I would say that most things in life are not perfect first time. As a student, I was developing my Mind Maps in real time while I was listening to the lecturer or reading a book. So I had no idea how the Mind Map would pan out. I didn't know when I started preparing it which part of the Mind Map might have the most or least information. I could find at the end of my study or lecture that there maybe too much information in one part of the Mind Map, eg the left hand section (in pink) of this Mind Map.

The solution was simple. I would just redo it when I got back to my student house, this time giving sufficient space to the key topics. I would then add in my images and pictures to help ensure it was visually appealing. Reworking a Mind Map a second time is no big deal. From my experience it helps commit information to memory and certainly beats re-reading sections of a heavy text book or writing things out again and again, hoping some information will stick.

Attainment .... Assessment of attainment ....

Sample of work in a test
In-tray exercises .... Work sample tools ....

- Attitudes
- Values
- Personality
  - Explicit
  - Implicit
.... Psychometric tests ....

Combination of different tools .... Assessment Centres ....

Train to do the job – how quickly they learn .... Trainability tests ....

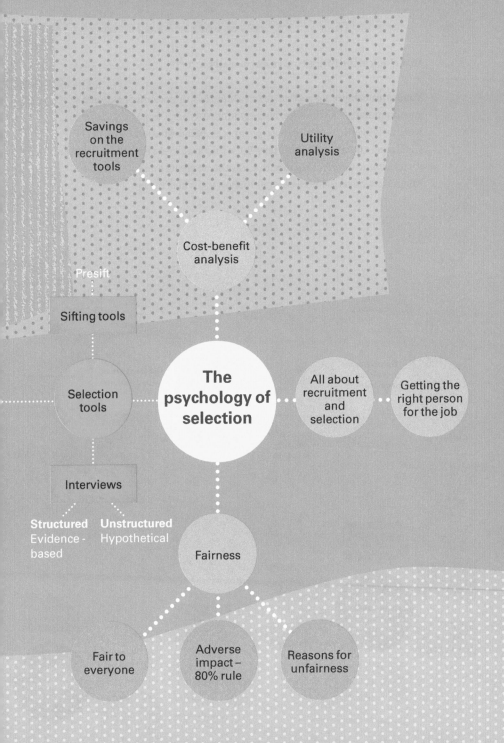

Savings on the recruitment tools

Utility analysis

Cost-benefit analysis

Presift

Sifting tools

The psychology of selection

All about recruitment and selection

Getting the right person for the job

Selection tools

Interviews

Structured Evidence-based

Unstructured Hypothetical

Fairness

Fair to everyone

Adverse impact – 80% rule

Reasons for unfairness

Interlock Mind Maps to give an overall picture

You are probably realising that just one Mind Map is not sufficient to allow you to summarise all the information you need to learn. Most of your exams will involve you having to learn large amounts of information. So it's likely you'll need a number of Mind Maps. But if they are all related to the same topic, it's possible to interlock them with each other to create a mosaic of Mind Maps. Here's a very simple example to show you what I mean:

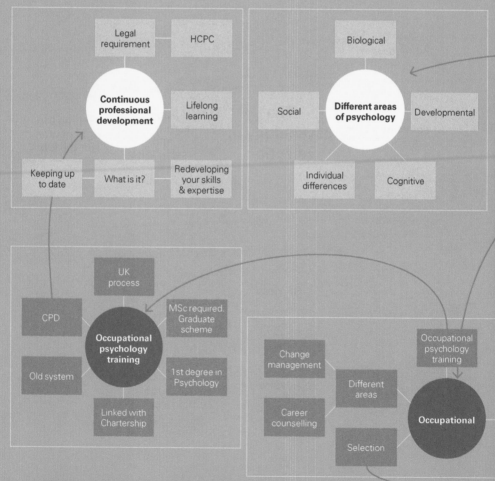

You will see I've got one key Mind Map in the middle and from this a number of other Mind Maps are placed around the periphery, but they are still related to the one in the middle. This mosaic of connected Mind Maps can be really helpful to aid our understanding and show the links between our different knowledge areas. I found this very useful in my exams when I could draw on important and related knowledge that might not have been immediately obvious, or if it was obvious, information I might have forgotten under the stress and pressure of exams.

TOP TIP

Interconnect different mind maps to create an overview of different knowledge areas.

Helps test individual differences

Psychological testing

Values

Selection ratio

Different tests

Attitude

Personality

Ability

Growing rapidly

Occupational

Clinical

Different professions

Psychology

Different areas of psychology

Forensic

What is it?

Study of the mind and behaviour

All about recruitment & selection

Selection

Psychological testing

Fairness

Different selection tools

Direct and Indirect discrimination

Interviews

What is it?

Application of psychology to work

Do Mind Maps really work?

When I was studying for my A levels in the late 70s and early 80s I had no knowledge of Mind Maps or memory techniques. I really struggled with studying. I would spend many hours just re-reading information, hoping it would stick. I sat my A level Biology exam three times before securing a low grade. I applied to Manchester Polytechnic and despite low grades they offered me a joint honours degree course in Psychology and Biology. I started my degree course and discovered memory techniques and Mind Maps. By the end of my first year I had secured two 'A' grades in Biology and had come towards the top of my year. I was the same person – the only thing that had changed was my memory techniques. I had translated my poor A level Biology grade at the third attempt into two top 'A' grades at polytechnic. So for me they really worked and they could really work for you too.

Try your own Mind Map

Now it's your turn. On page 99 opposite, there is some fictitious information about a range of phone apps that, let's say, you need to learn and memorise for a Communication exam. Have a go at taking the information and preparing your own Mind Map. You may want to re-read the advice about Mind Maps and how to prepare them from page 92. Remember that your first Mind Map may not be perfect so you might have to rework it before preparing your final version – you could always start by making a draft or sketch.

You will need

Flip chart paper/A3 size paper
A collection of pens/pencils of
different colours
Lots of imagination!

Remember to:

TOP TIP

As you build up your knowledge base, your mind maps will grow too.

- Put the main title in the middle, with key points radiating out from the title like a spider's web.
- Interconnect different points on the Mind Map with lines.
- Use colour and draw pictures to make it visually appealing
- Make your Mind Map distinctive, bizarre and funny.

The magic phone apps

Interconnect Phone Apps Ltd (IPA) are a company based in the UK.

Their co-founders were Billy Marshall and Audrey Steddon who set the company up in 1983. They have a London-based office, and offices around the world including Hong Kong, China, Singapore, America (California), Stockholm in Sweden and Dublin in Ireland. Sales in 1993 were £20,000. In 2012 they reported sales of £4.5 million.

Audrey Steddon was a professional magician before forming IPA with her brother. IPA now have 232 phone apps that are all about how to do magic. All phone apps are available in English; half are available in Cantonese and Swedish. There are 10 magic phone apps that have been designed for children to learn how to do magic. The remainder of the phone apps have been designed for adults. These have been categorised into magic for beginners, intemediates and experts. Each phone app includes at least one magic trick. Each of the children's magic phone apps has at least three magic tricks.

The phone apps have been written in Dezel computer language, with the Apricot operating system supplied by Sterimet, based in California. Some of the earlier phone apps were written in Pava but these are being upgraded into Dezel – this will be complete in two years' time.

Billy Marshall is a computer programmer and wrote all the software himself from 1993 until 2008. When the company was formed, the magic tricks software was written for PC use. However, with the growth of phone apps, this has now been phased out. IPA are now working on a new generation of phone apps for the games market, including automation of the well-known Twizzle, Ganderbit and Hideaway board games used by children and adults alike. The biggest and growing market for IPA is China where sales have increased by 300% in just two years.

How did you get on?

How did you get on preparing your Mind Map? Did you find it easy or difficult? Did you enjoy preparing it?

Mind Maps give you the opportunity to cut down a lot of written text into some manageable key points that are presented in a visual format. Having it presented in this way means it will be much easier to learn and memorise. Preparing good Mind Maps is a real life skill that has to be developed through practice. When you first start out, it might take a little work and some effort – both to create the Mind Map and to ensure that it is ingrained in your memory. But it has the potential to really enhance your learning power and could provide you with rich rewards.

Testing your learning

In this workbook I have given you a range of building blocks that can help improve your memory. I've also provided you with a selection of key and lock memory techniques to help you learn more effectively.

Let's say you are revising for an exam. You have understood everything in the syllabus and you have applied the best techniques for you from this workbook to help you remember the information. So what's next? You need to test your memory to see how good your recall is. Here are some tips on how to do that:

1. Leave a couple of hours between learning and testing. See how much you can remember from memory by just thinking about it or writing it down on a piece of paper.

2. Once you've remembered as much as you can, go back to your notes or mind maps etc and see how you did.

3. Give yourself a pat on the back for the information you remembered well.

4. Identify those things that you've forgotten. Have a think about why you might have forgotten them. What do you think you could do to help you remember those things better? This might include using some more of the techniques that we've already discussed in this workbook, ie:

    –   Using more imagery.
    –   Using more colour.
    –   Making the information more bizarre and distinctive.
    –   Making sure you understand it.
    –   Making it more understandable by breaking it down into bitesize chunks. (Remember the dinosaur in Building Block 5 on page 60.)
    –   Using a better key and lock technique that works for you.
    –   Making a stronger link between your key and its lock.
    –   Using a Mind Map rather than other techniques that we have explored in this workbook.

5. Once you've identified what you could do to improve your memory, make those improvements and re-learn the information. Once again after a period of time, test your memory to see whether the improvements have worked and your recall has increased. This is all part of the process of continuous improvement.

Over to you

Decide what works for you

Now that you've completed this workbook, you may well find that some of the techniques and building blocks work better for you than others. That's only to be expected. What I've tried to do is give you a choice of options so you can decide what works for you.

Try them out and persevere

In the past you may have been used to studying and learning in a particular way. This is likely to be very familiar to you and comfortable. The tools and techniques in this workbook may be new to you. So using them might feel uncomfortable and unfamiliar, but my advice would be to try them out and persevere. The benefits could be enormous for you in helping you to remember more in your exams. This in turn could help you improve your exam success generally, giving you that competitive edge. Ultimately, that could lead to your golden job opportunity or a sought-after university course.

Small, but significant improvements

The worst-case scenario might be that the tools and techniques we've explored together in this workbook might only bring a small improvement in your learning power and your memory performance. Let's say you also make other small improvements in your studying techniques, such as:

- Reading around your subject.
- Making the effort to look up the most recent research.
- Setting up study buddy groups with your friends and colleagues.
- Learning to manage stress more effectively.
- Getting extra support from your family and friends.

Combine these with your small memory improvement and collectively they could create a big difference in your exam performance and therefore your success.

This reminds me of the discussions that took place about the reasons for Great Britain's success in Cycling in the 2012 London Olympics. It would appear there was no magic bullet. Instead it was just an accumulation of small but significant improvements in many things that touched the athlete and impacted on his or her performance. As Dave Brailsford, Team GB Cycling Performance Director said:

"It was attention to detail that gave us the advantage over the other teams. We considered everything, even the smallest improvements, to give us a competitive edge. It was the accumulation of these small details that made us unbeatable."

References

Murdock, BB, *The serial position effect of free recall, Journal of Experimental Psychology, Vol 64(5)*, 1962, pp482–488. Page 16

Craik, FIM, Lockhart, RS, *Levels of Processing: A Framework for Memory Research, Journal of Verbal Learning and Verbal Behavior, Vol 11*, 1972, pp671–684. Page 32

Interference theory explaining the process of forgetting: Visit http://www.simplypsychology.org/forgetting by Saul McLeod. Page 43

Shepard, RN, *Recognition memory for words, sentences and pictures, Journal of Verbal Learning and Verbal Behavior, Vol 6*, 1967. Page 58

Method of Loci: Visit http://en.wikipedia.org/wiki/method-of-loci. Page 72

c.1648, Stanislaus Mink von Wennsshein is thought to be one of the first to put forward the 'major system' which is an idea for using numbers as a memory technique. For more information visit: https://en.wikipedia.org/wiki/Stanislaus_Mink_von_Wennsshein. Page 77.

Mind Mapping created by Tony Buzan: Visit http://thinkbuzan.com. Page 90

Notes

Notes

Lightning Source UK Ltd.
Milton Keynes UK
UKOW06f0055250216

269085UK00009B/27/P